NOW HEAR THIS, PREPARE TO COMMENCE
READING THE *1998 ACTION MAN ANNUAL*.
HELP ME HUNT DOWN THE EVIL DOCTOR X
BEFORE DISASTER STRIKES ON THE FEARSOME
OMEGA MISSION!
STAY EXTREME!

Action Man Annual is published
under licence from 3D Licensing Ltd.
by
Pedigree Books
The Old Rectory, Matford LAne,
Exeter EX2 4PS

LOCKED TOGETHER ON THE SWAYING CARRIAGE ROOF...

...THE SLIGHTEST SHIFT IN BALANCE WOULD SEND ONE OF US OVER THE SIDE.

NO PUNCHES.

NO KICKS.

NO SNARLING THREATS.

BUT MAKE NO MISTAKE—

THIS WAS A FIGHT TO THE DEATH.

DR X WAS QUIETER THAN USUAL.

I BLAMED IT ON HIS FEAR OF FALLING OFF THE TRAIN.

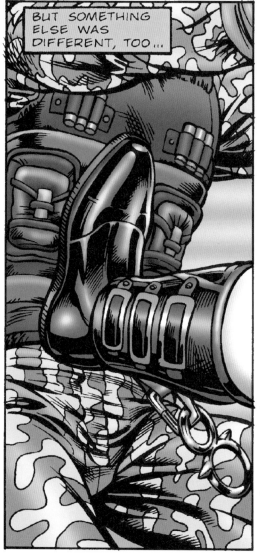

BUT SOMETHING ELSE WAS DIFFERENT, TOO...

...SOMETHING ABOUT THE WAY HE MOVED.

WHOAAA!

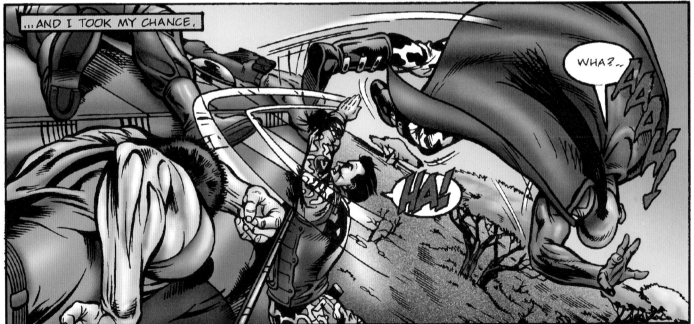

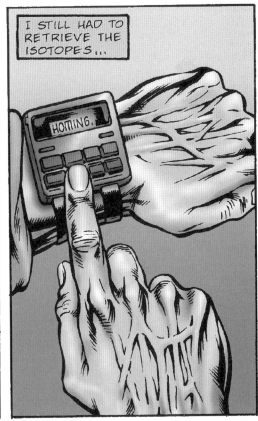

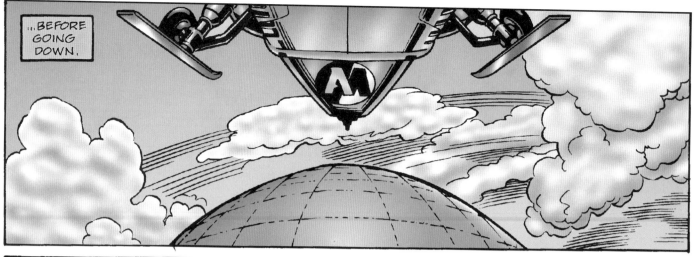

THIRTY THOUSAND FEET UP AND NOWHERE TO GO...

MISSILE FIRING MECHANISM = ARMED.

...BUT DOWN.

I COULDN'T RISK ARMING THE MISSILES AND DESTROYING THE ISOTOPES...

WHAT?

GET DOWN!

OH NO!

HE'LL KILL US ALL!

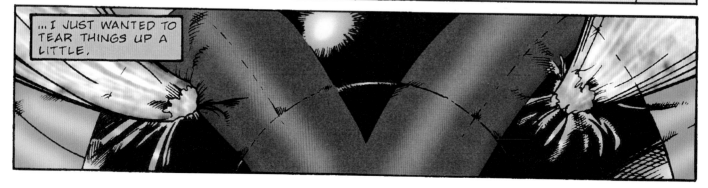

...I JUST WANTED TO TEAR THINGS UP A LITTLE.

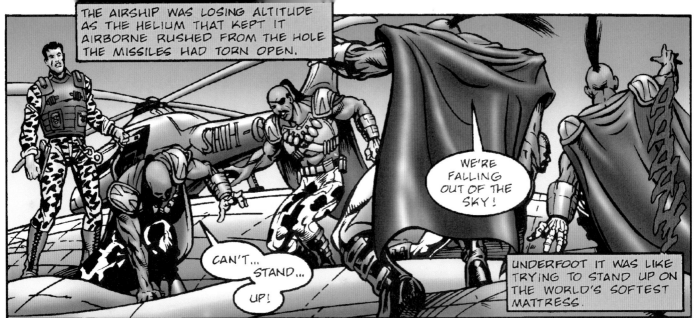

THE AIRSHIP WAS LOSING ALTITUDE AS THE HELIUM THAT KEPT IT AIRBORNE RUSHED FROM THE HOLE THE MISSILES HAD TORN OPEN.

WE'RE FALLING OUT OF THE SKY!

CAN'T... STAND... UP!

UNDERFOOT IT WAS LIKE TRYING TO STAND UP ON THE WORLD'S SOFTEST MATTRESS.

ALL I HAD TO DO WAS WAIT

KLIK!

...WAIT FOR THE REAL DR X TO SHOW HIMSELF!

NO!

SAVE US!

COME BACK, MASTER!

BLAST YOU, ACTION MAN!

SOMETHING ELSE I HAVE LEARNT OVER MY YEARS FIGHTING DR X...

...AS WELL AS BEING THE MOST EVIL MAN IN THE WORLD...

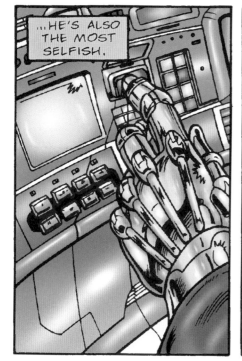

...HE'S ALSO THE MOST SELFISH.

DR X DIDN'T SURVIVE SO LONG BY CARING ABOUT HIS FOLLOWERS' HEALTH AND WELL BEING...

...AND I DIDN'T HAVE TIME.

THE ISOTOPES WERE MY TOP PRIORITY.

AND I WASN'T GOING TO LET HIM GET AWAY!

AS HE FLEW ACROSS THE CABIN, DR X MADE A GRAB FOR THE ISOTOPES...

KERRRASH!

AAAAAII!

HA! HA! BETTER LUCK NEXT TIME, ACTION MAN... ...BUT THERE WON'T BE A NEXT TIME!

FRUSTRATED, ALL I COULD DO WAS GUIDE THE GLIDER EARTHWARD.

I WONDERED WHAT DR X HAD PLANNED FOR THE ISOTOPES...

HE DIDN'T WASTE ANY TIME LETTING THE WORLD KNOW.

THE ISOTOPES ARE NOW PART OF THE MOST POWERFUL LASER SATELLITE IN THE WORLD!

UNLESS THE NATIONS OF THE WORLD KNEEL BEFORE ME...

...THEIR CAPITAL CITIES WILL BURN!

GLOBAL MONITORING SYSTEM
ONLINE

FROM: UNITED NATIONS SECURITY COUNCIL
TO: ACTION MAN
YOUR NEW MISSION: STOP DR X BLACKMAILING THE WORLD.

ACTION MAN
INTELLIGENCE TEST

This annual contains several pages designed to test your mission aptitude. This is your first test. The two pictures below are exactly the same... almost. There are eight vital differences between them. Can you spot them all?

Answers on page 109.

WANTED!
FOR CRIMES AGAINST HUMANITY
DOCTOR X

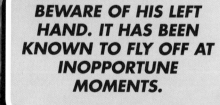

BEWARE OF HIS LEFT HAND. IT HAS BEEN KNOWN TO FLY OFF AT INOPPORTUNE MOMENTS.

REAL NAME: UNKNOWN
AGE: UNKNOWN
BARBER: UNKNOWN
KNOWN ACCOMPLICES:
THE SKULLMEN, SCHOOL BULLIES, GIRLS.
KNOWN METHODS:
THEFT, BRIBERY, CORRUPTION, BLACK-MAIL, LARCENY, ANYTHING. YOU NAME IT, HE'S DONE IT.

REWARD(S):
TOO MANY TO LIST HERE. CAPTURE DOCTOR X, DEAD OR ALIVE, AND PREPARE TO BE HONOURED BY EVERY NATION IN THE WORLD!

SURVIVAL TIPS:
HOT CLIMATES

On secret missions in hot climates, I have to take precautions. Undercover work in Africa isn't like a day at the beach. Not only do I have to watch out for Dr X and his Skullmen; the weather itself can be my worst enemy.

HEAT

Sometimes it's easier to rest during the day and work at night. Keep your skin covered where possible to avoid sun burn. Protect exposed areas with sun cream.

WATER

In the desert you need water more than you need food! Carry plenty of fresh, clean water with you. Never drink from a stream or river; the water could be polluted. Also, watch out for dry riverbeds, or wadis. If you pitch your camp in one of these, you could be washed away if it suddenly starts to rain.

WILD ANIMALS

These creatures aren't pets. Assume that 'wild' means 'dangerous' and stay away. It's not just the danger of lions, tigers or other big cats mistaking you for their lunch. Herbivorous animals can be just as dangerous if they forget you're there. Giraffes or elephants can stampede and trample you if they are frightened. If you have to sneak past animals, pretend they are enemy soldiers KEEP QUIET.

DATA FILE:
THE ACTION MAN LSV

In the harsh, unforgiving terrain of the wilderness, my LIGHT SUPPORT VEHICLE (LSV) is crucial. On land, and even in the swamp, this is no ordinary car.

GUN ON SWIVEL MOUNT

Unless you have a team member with you in the LSV, this can be difficult to operate while the LSV is in motion. (Although I did once keep driving with my feet, it's not recommended). Use the LSV to keep a distance, shoot at your target and then get away before they can return fire.

POWERFUL HEADLAMPS

There are no streetlights in the middle of nowhere. If you try and find your way around in the dark, you'll need all the help you can get.

OVERSIZED TYRES

High off the ground for rocky roads and crossing small streams. Note the heavy suspension to prevent axle damage.

LARGE AERIAL

Very important to keep in touch with other team members at all times. The radio on the LSV has a range of over 100 miles.

TOP SECRET!

The LSV can also be converted for swamp mobility.
But note the large, powerful propeller engine. It is very noisy and definitely NOT suitable for sneak attacks.

ROLL CAGE

Even if you crash, the roll bars prevent the driver from getting too badly hurt. Careful though, you can still end up with some painful bruises.

OUT OF AFRICA

There was nothing to see. There was nothing to hear. Just a few fishing boats on the Indian Ocean, plodding home with the catch of the day. Suddenly, there was the sound of a terrific, rolling explosion. The breeze rushed briefly but settled down again. The fishermen looked up, expecting to see thunder clouds in the sky, but it was a clear summer's day.

Action Man was already sixty miles away at the controls of his plane. Radar proof, and too fast to see, all he left in his wake was a sonic boom as the air itself rushed to keep up with him. Dr X's blimp was just like its criminal owner: slow, inflated and full of gas. It would get him nowhere fast. As for the helicopter, it had its uses, but its range was too short and it was already low on fuel.

He guessed he'd be needed in Asia, but Action Man never really guessed anything. He knew the satellite's orbit would take it east, and he knew the UN wouldn't let it stay in the sky for much longer.

This seemed as good a place as any. As the stealth fighter banked sharply to follow the steep mountain range, Action Man ejected the supplies he'd crammed into the cargo area. As they fell towards the ground, he set the plane on auto and jumped out after them. His parachute opened with a snap and he guided it back down. Back toward the ground. Back into danger.

MISSION OMEGA

PART TWO

THE UNITED NATIONS SECURITY COUNCIL CO-ORDINATED THE SEARCH FOR DR X'S DEADLY SATELLITE.

EARTH BOUND MONITORING STATIONS AROUND THE WORLD SEARCHED THE SKY. REPORTS FLASHED THROUGH ULTRA-SECURE COMMUNICATIONS NETWORKS: THE SATELLITE HAD BEEN LOCATED!

FLOATING THOUSANDS OF MILES ABOVE THE EARTH, DR X'S SATELLITE WAS AWAITING IT'S CREATOR'S COMMAND TO UNLEASH ITS POWER!

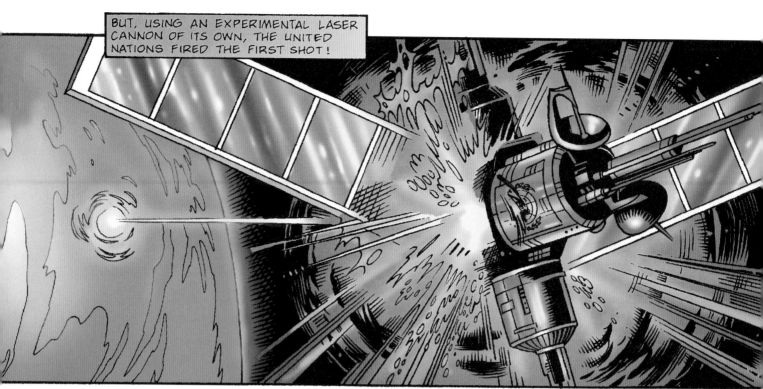

BUT, USING AN EXPERIMENTAL LASER CANNON OF ITS OWN, THE UNITED NATIONS FIRED THE FIRST SHOT!

THE TRACKING STATIONS THAT HAD LOCATED THE SATELLITE NOW FOLLOWED ITS DESCENT.

THE SATELLITE CRASH-LANDED IN THE HIMALAYAS. FROM THE MOMENT IT LANDED, IT WAS A RACE AGAINST TIME...

...THE REST OF THE WORLD AGAINST DR X!

MOVE IT, YOU GUYS!

WE'VE BEEN TRAMPING ALL OVER THESE MOUNTAINS AN' I'M SICK OF THIS COLD!

NIGHT CLOSED IN.

THERE WAS NO TIME TO REST.

I HAD TO CATCH UP WITH X'S MEN BEFORE THEY UNLOADED THE ISOTOPES...

...OR ELSE I'D BE LEFT WITH AN EXPENSIVE PIECE OF SPACE JUNK.

MY MISSION HAD BECOME MORE DIFFICULT THAN I HAD EXPECTED...

...BUT I HAD THE EQUIPMENT— AND THE DETERMINATION— TO RESCUE THE SITUATION!

MY LUCK WAS HOLDING ...

THE SNOW HAD NOT COVERED THE TRACKS LEFT BY X'S MEN.

THEY THOUGHT I WAS DEAD, THEY WERE WRONG.

THEY THOUGHT THEIR MISSION WAS A SUCCESS...

...THEY WERE WRONG.

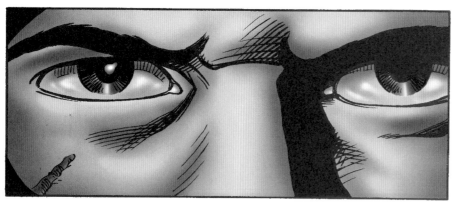

I FOLLOWED THEIR TRAIL, BUT STOPPED SHORT OF THEIR HIDEOUT.

I HAD GONE HEAD-TO-HEAD WITH THEM ONCE. I WASN'T GOING TO MAKE THAT MISTAKE AGAIN.

FROM THE LOOK OF THINGS, THEY HAD SETTLED IN FOR THE NIGHT.

THERE WAS NO SIGN OF THE SATELLITE. IT HAD TO BE LOCKED IN THERE WITH THEM.

IT WOULD BE TOO RISKY TO AIR-LIFT THE ISOTOPES AT NIGHT...

NIGHT VISION: ON 500M

...BUT I DECIDED TO MAKE SURE. FIRST, I TRANSMITTED A STATUS REPORT TO THE SECURITY COUNCIL...

...THEN I MADE ANOTHER CALL.

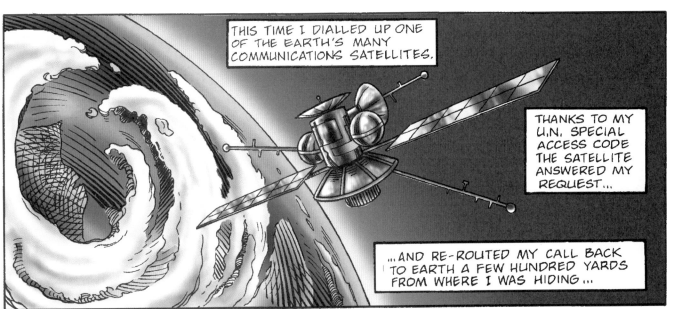

THIS TIME I DIALLED UP ONE OF THE EARTH'S MANY COMMUNICATIONS SATELLITES.

THANKS TO MY U.N. SPECIAL ACCESS CODE THE SATELLITE ANSWERED MY REQUEST...

...AND RE-ROUTED MY CALL BACK TO EARTH A FEW HUNDRED YARDS FROM WHERE I WAS HIDING...

...TO DR X'S SATELLITE!

I'M IN!

X-SAT CPU-ACCESS APPROVED.

I HAD HOPED TO FIND A WAY TO NEUTRALIZE THE SATELLITE'S DEADLY CARGO WITHOUT TAKING ON DR X'S HEAVIES.

I DISCOVERED SOMETHING MORE INTERESTING ...

...AND MORE AT DEADLY!

SELF DESTRUCT ARMED: 5:00

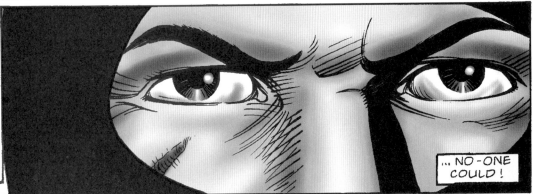

DR X MUST HAVE GOT BORED OF WAITING, HE HAD ACTIVATED THE SATELLITE'S SELF-DESTRUCT MECHANISM, HE WANTED TO MAKE SURE THAT, IF HE COULDN'T HAVE THE ISOTOPES...

...NO-ONE COULD!

SELF DESTRUCT
IN
04 MINUTES
50 SECONDS

KLAK!

KLIK!

IF I HAD TO
GO IN THERE...

...IT WOULD BE ON
MY OWN TERMS.

ACTION MAN
INTELLIGENCE TEST

This mission took place in the **HIMALAYAS**, the tall range of **MOUNTAINS** where the legendary Abominable Snowman (or **YETI**) is said to live. Bordered by **INDIA** on one side and **TIBET** on the others, the range of **PEAKS** includes the highest mountain in the world, Mount **EVEREST**. The local people keep goats and **LLAMAS** on the lower slopes, where it is quite warm, but as you venture higher the air becomes so thin that you need to bring your own **OXYGEN** for breathing. Local bearers, or sherpas, can help adventurers carry their equipment up. A good **SHERPA** is worth his weight in gold.

Can you find the words in **CAPITALS** in the puzzle below?
Answers on page 109.

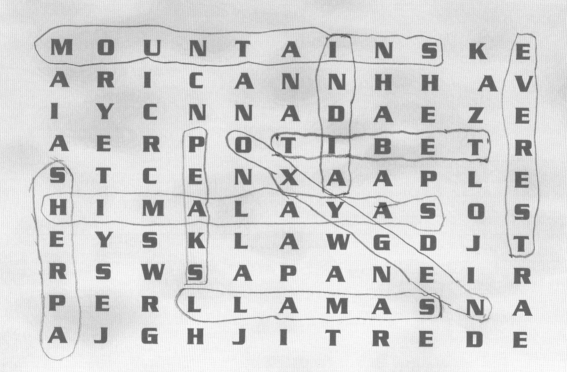

DATA FILE:
SCUBA DIVER

DIVING KNIFE
For cutting through snags and underwater nets.

FLIPPERS
For extra power when swimming. Can double my speed.

WET SUIT
Keeps me warm underwater.

AQUALUNG
For long periods underwater. Contains up to 2 hours of compressed air.

HARPOON
Uses compressed air to shoot a silent, deadly dart. Useful in underwater combat. It can take a while to reload, so shoot carefully.

COLOUR SCHEME
Orange/yellow and black is nature's way of showing that a fish is dangerous. It might just scare a shark away!

WEIGHTS
The air in the human body makes it float naturally. The weights help keep me down on the sea bed. I can cut them loose for a quick get-away.

SNORKEL
For shorter dives. Not recommended for combat situations. The enemy might spot the snorkel poking above the waves.

DATA FILE:
SNOWBOARD RAIDER

Snowboarding is rough, tough and dangerous, but luckily, so am I.

CRASH HELMET

There are plenty of hazards on the mountainside. This helmet doesn't only stop me from knocking myself out. It also contains a limited air supply in case I find myself too high up.

GAUNTLETS

Keeping my fingers exposed is a big risk for frostbite, but I need to be able to do delicate work.

RIFLE

I use a low calibre rifle in snow settings because it makes less noise. One loud bang too many and I could bring an avalanche down on my head.

SKI JACKET

It's warm, but more importantly, it's also light. Mountains may have snow at the top, but if the bottom is in a hot country, I won't need the jacket until I'm high up on the slopes. This jacket is light enough to carry in my pack until I need it.

ICE CUTTER

For cutting through ice, obviously. And also for hacking my way through dense forest.

CRASH PADS

In case I fall off the board, these pads will protect my elbows and knees.

HEAVY BOOTS

All that twisting and turning can damage my ankles. These boots keep my feet relatively steady, and warm, too!

ACTION MAN INTELLIGENCE TEST

The Skullmen are too stupid to know that they will cause an avalanche if they shoot at Action Man on his snowboard. Can you guide Action Man down the mountain without running into one of Dr X's men?

Answer on page 109.

SILENT RUNNING

The hang-glider lay broken on the shore of the lake. Action Man finished putting on his wetsuit and glanced back before he jumped into the water. It was a shame he had to dump it here, but there was no time to lose. There were lights in the hills above; X's men were already tailing him.

He sank beneath the surface. The water was murky and cold, he could barely see past his hand and it was too risky to use a torch. Even if he stayed low and silent, it was possible that the bubbles from his aqualung would give him away. Time was short.

His hands found the mud that covered the bottom of the lake. He felt his way along, hoping against hope that his plan would work. He felt the backwash as unseen fish danced out of his path. His hands snagged on underwater weeds... on a large rock... on... on.. a familiar metal casing. His stealth fighter! It had splashed down here as instructed.

Several of X's Skullmen reached the shore of the lake and peered into the water in search of tell-tale signs of their prey. One pointed in surprise at a huge mass of bubbles rising to the surface from the middle of the lake. The men raised their guns, but were thrown back as the Stealth fighter powered out of the water and into the air.

Action Man waved at them from the cockpit and cut in the afterburners, heading east at full power. The Skullmen were soon left far behind him. For them, justice would have to wait. Action Man had bigger fish to fry.

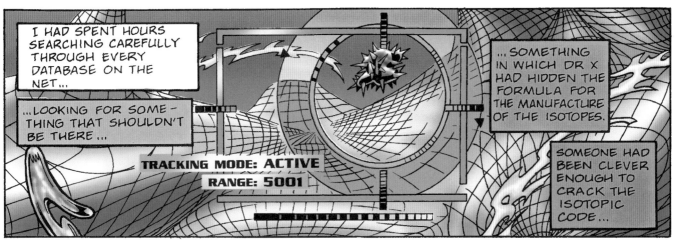

I HAD SPENT HOURS SEARCHING CAREFULLY THROUGH EVERY DATABASE ON THE NET...

...LOOKING FOR SOMETHING THAT SHOULDN'T BE THERE...

TRACKING MODE: ACTIVE
RANGE: 5001

...SOMETHING IN WHICH DR X HAD HIDDEN THE FORMULA FOR THE MANUFACTURE OF THE ISOTOPES.

SOMEONE HAD BEEN CLEVER ENOUGH TO CRACK THE ISOTOPIC CODE...

...CLEVER BUT UNLUCKY.

I-I DON'T UNDER-STAND!

I DID WHAT YOU ASKED ME TO DO...

I BROKE THE ISOTOPIC CODE...

...BUT NOW YOU TREAT ME LIKE I'D DONE SOMETHING AGAINST YOU!

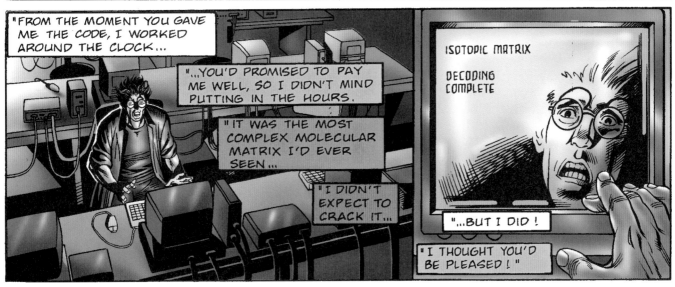

"FROM THE MOMENT YOU GAVE ME THE CODE, I WORKED AROUND THE CLOCK...

"...YOU'D PROMISED TO PAY ME WELL, SO I DIDN'T MIND PUTTING IN THE HOURS.

"IT WAS THE MOST COMPLEX MOLECULAR MATRIX I'D EVER SEEN...

"I DIDN'T EXPECT TO CRACK IT...

ISOTOPIC MATRIX

DECODING COMPLETE

"...BUT I DID !

"I THOUGHT YOU'D BE PLEASED !"

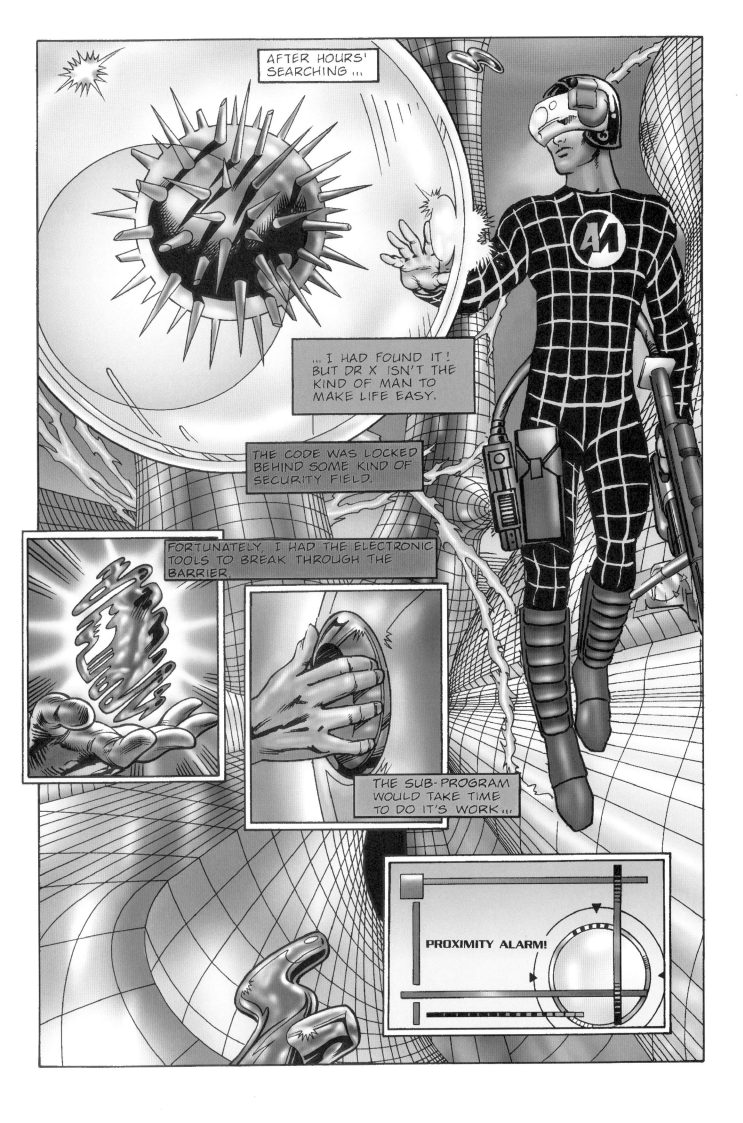

I'D HAD ENOUGH OF RUNNING.

MOUNTED IN MY VIRTUAL WEAPON WAS A SHORT-RANGE WARP GENERATOR ...

...MY ATTACKER'S VIRTUAL ARMOUR COULDN'T HANDLE THE STRAIN AS THE FABRIC OF CYBERSPACE BUCKED AND TWISTED AROUND THEM.

FOR DR X'S MEN, THE GAME WAS DEFINITELY OVER!

JEEZ!

HE'S *TOO* FAST!

THERE'S NO TIME TO WASTE...

...I'VE GOT A DATE WITH AN ISOTOPE!

A CLOSE CONTACT DATA MINE.

SMALL...

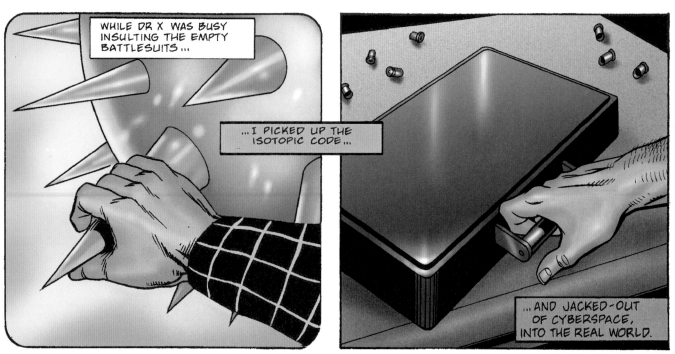

WHILE DR X WAS BUSY INSULTING THE EMPTY BATTLESUITS...

...I PICKED UP THE ISOTOPIC CODE...

...AND JACKED-OUT OF CYBERSPACE, INTO THE REAL WORLD.

MY GOOD LUCK WAS THEIR BAD LUCK.

TAKING MY POWERBOOK WITH ME, I HURRIED DOWN THE BACK STAIRS.

FIRE EXIT

FIRE EXIT

WHO...?

DID DR X SEND BACK-UP?

ACTION MAN
INTELLIGENCE TEST

There are eight very important differences between these two pictures. Can you spot them all?

Answers on page 109.

SURVIVAL TIPS:
COLD CLIMATES

And you thought Africa was tough? There are just as many hazards which can affect missions in cold weather. Memorise these points to avoid endangering yourself and your mission teams.

WRAP UP WARM

It might only feel slightly chilly, but remember you could be out on your mission for a long while.

KEEP DRY

Snow is only dry because it is cold. If it gets close to your body (through your sleeves for example, or down the collar of your jacket) it will turn to water again. Avoid at all costs. Shivering and discomfort may distract you for vital seconds and jeopardise the mission.

ICE

Watch where you walk. If you tread on a patch of ice you could slip over and give away your location. Never go near frozen ponds or lakes. It might look like a good shortcut to speed up the mission, but the risk of falling through thin ice is too great. If you want to play around on the ice for fun, do what I do and go to an ice rink.

THE ACTION MAN HANG

There's more than one way to get down a mountain fast, but they don't come much faster than the hang-glider featured here. Made in several easily-folded pieces, it can be carried in a large backpack and deployed when necessary. And with no noise or extra weight from the engine, it can carry you far and fast, the ultimate in low-tech stealth. Please pay attention to the safety restrictions below to avoid dangerous mid-mission disasters.

WINGS:

Made from a light, strong artificial fibre. Warning: the wings bullet-proof. Avoid enemy contact while airborne.

SUPPORT STRUTS

Made of strong, hollow aluminium, they are easy to carry and assemble. Warning: the wings must be symmetrical at all times. Take care not to bend the struts during assembly or it will hamper the hang-glider's speed and ease of control. Take care while landing for the same reason. If you need to make a quick getaway and your wings were damaged in the last landing, you may be forced to defend yourself on the ground from unknown numbers of Skullmen.

PILOT HARNESS

Ensure that all clips are attached and secure. The hang-glider is steered by your body, and your legs must be straight out behind you to facilitate control.

ot

DATA FILE:
HELIGUN

For close combat operations, a plane is virtually useless. By the time you can see the target, you're already flying past it. Planes also require a decent-sized runway to land, but I've landed this helicopter gunship in some pretty tight places.

ROTORS
There's more than one use for sharp, spinning blades of metal. These don't just keep me in the air, they can be used to clear trees away for emergency landings in jungle clearings. It makes one hell of a racket though.

STEALTH BODYWORK
This special non-reflective material remains top secret. The proof of its value lies in what it does to enemy radar: NOTHING! Dr X's minions don't know I'm sneaking up on them until its too late.

TAIL ROTOR
This is the only thing that keeps the helicopter from spinning out of control, and so it's heavily protected by these metal bars.

WHISPER ENGINE
Heavily insulated to cut the noise right down, criminals have been known to mistake the sound of my helicopter for a car revving up in the next street.

NYPD BLUES

It was lunchtime at the thirteenth precinct, and Dennis was getting ready to tuck into a whole box of doughnuts. And this time, he wouldn't be offering them to anyone else. Especially not Jimmy, who never got fat, no matter how many he ate.

Then Jimmy had made him come out on this stupid call. Some weirdo in a purple outfit had tipped them off about a theft going down on the south side. And here he was, getting out of the squad car when he should be in the nice warm office having another coffee.

Dennis wanted this over as quickly as possible. Bust the door down, snap on the handcuffs, and drag the crooks back to the squad house. That's if there was a robbery at all; Amy at the front desk had told him that the tip-off came from a guy who looked like he was in fancy dress. If this was a joke, there would be hell to pay.

The building looked innocent enough. But there was a seriously cool red sportscar parked outside. That wasn't normal. What kind of crook would drive a set of wheels like that? Dennis took a long hard look at the badge on the hood. It was an orange and black design, and it looked strangely familiar.

'You sure this is the right place?' asked Dennis.

Dennis and Jimmy both ducked as the unmistakeable sound of gunfire tore through the street. Someone was shooting inside the building!

'Let's get inside!' shouted Jimmy to the other cops. 'Something's going down!'

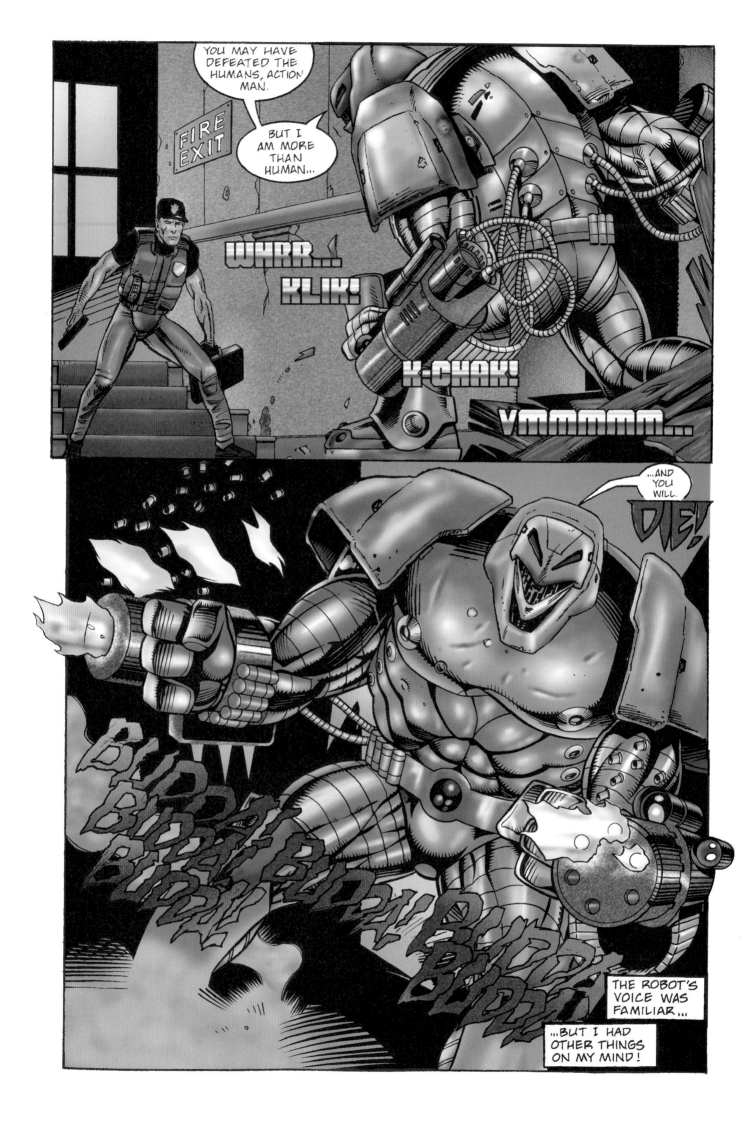

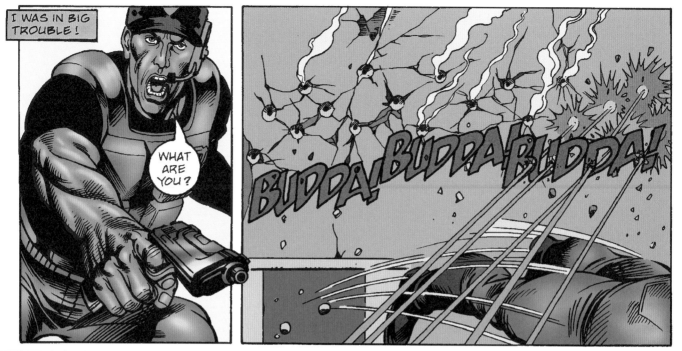

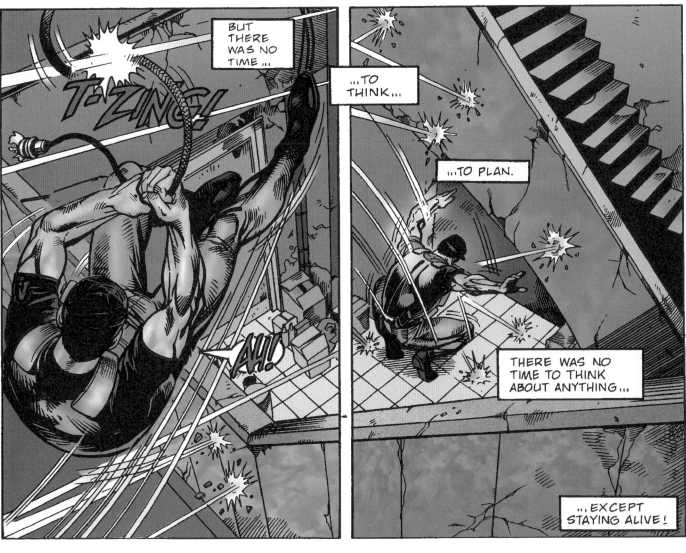

ACTION MAN, YOU HAVE ALWAYS BEEN BRAVE AND RESOURCEFUL...

...BUT NOW YOU HIDE LIKE A CRAVEN COWARD!

COME OUT OF THERE AND DIE LIKE A MAN!

ROBOT THIS IS A VERY OLD BUILDING.

IT'S WALLS ARE ALREADY WEAK AND CRUMBLING...

KREAK!

GROAN!

NO!

...YOUR GUNFIRE HAS ONLY WEAKENED THEM EVEN FURTHER.

YOU CALL ME A COWARD...

...BUT I PREFER TO THINK...

...THAT I HAVE THE GOOD SENSE TO AVOID SEVERAL TONS OF FALLING BUILDING!

I HAD NO IDEA WHETHER THE ROBOT WAS OUT OF ACTION...

...SENT BY DR X TO KILL ME WHILE I WAS IN *CYBERSPACE*...

...I'D NEED SOME BACK UP OF MY OWN.

* SEE LAST ISSUE FOR FULL MISSION REPORT.

MY PLAN WAS TO FIND SOME SPACE...

...THEN CALL IN REINFORCE-MENTS...

OKAY, PAL...

...SO MUCH FOR THAT IDEA.

FREEZE!

GENTLE-MEN, YOU WILL NOT BELIEVE THIS!

"...AND I'LL TRY TO ENLIGHTEN YOU!

WHAT ARE YOU TALKING AB-- AAAHHH!

AH--AAAHHH!

I CAN'T SEE!

THE FLASH GRENADE CONCEALED IN THE CASE WAS ONLY MEANT TO DAZZLE AND STUN...

IF THEY WEREN'T GOING TO LISTEN TO ME...

HEY!

EVERYTHING'S SPINNING!

...I HAVE TO FIND SOMEONE WHO WILL LISTEN!

I HAD TO FIND SOMEONE IN AUTHORITY, WARN THEM ABOUT THE ROBOT...

...BUT THAT DIDN'T STOP IT!

NO!

PLEASE!

DON'T!

I...I...AAA

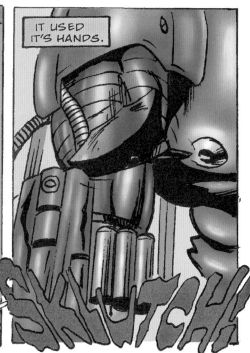

IT USED IT'S HANDS.

SKNUTCH!

SO

WHO'S NEXT?

ROBOTS ARE SUPPOSED TO BE COLD MACHINES...

...UNTHINKING, UNFEELING...

...NOT THIS ONE.

DOC EX

AS I WATCHED IT ATTACK THE POLICEMEN, I COULD TELL...

...IT WAS ENJOYING ITSELF!

DR X'S MEN HAD TRANSPORTED THE ROBOT IN A HEAVILY MODIFIED VAN...

LUCKY FOR ME, THEY HAD LEFT THE KEYS IN THE INGNITION.

I HOPED TO TURN THOSE MODIFICATIONS TO MY ADVANTAGE !

UNFORTUNATELY, THE HEAVY ARTILLERY HAD NO EFFECT ON THE ROBOTS METAL HIDE.

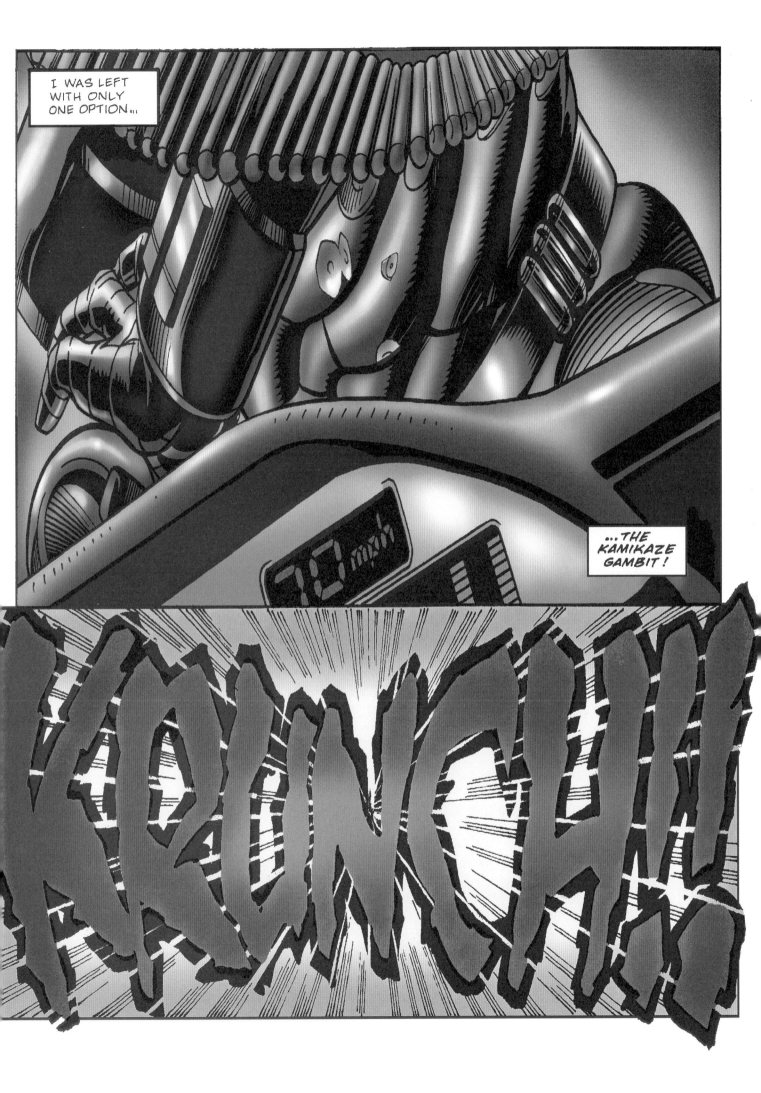

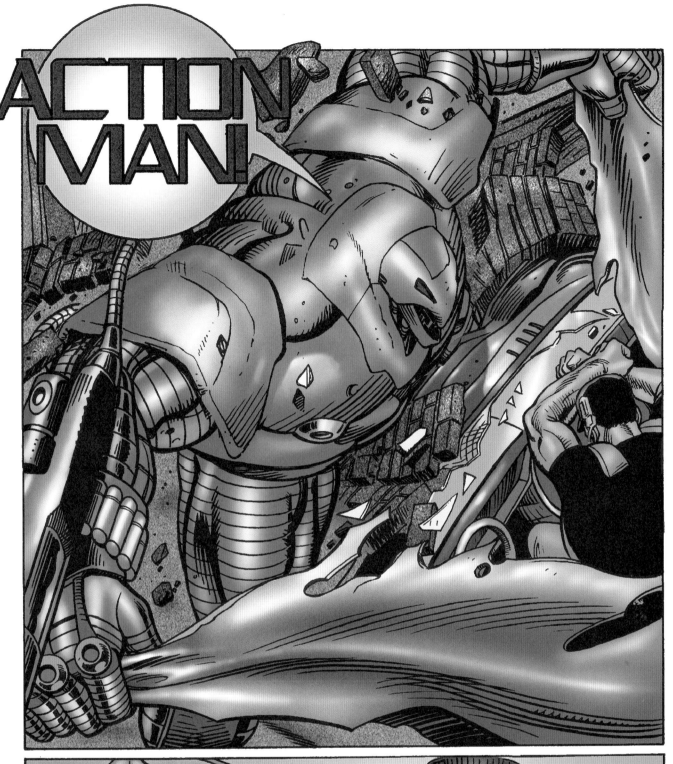

ACTION MAN
INTELLIGENCE TEST

Someone has infected Action Man's computer with a virus.
Now all he can see is a screen full of numbers. But there is a message in the
numbers, which reveals the culprit. Can you crack the anti-virus code and
join up the right digits to read the message?

ANTI-VIRUS CODE: 7 + 8 ÷ 3 = ?

```
29381731823194101019407123787897887012831981029381209310029381023
93810231038102938019789789789789797810194071287109401270128319831
98102938120931002938102938182310381029380192382938173182319410101
94071094012702871094012701283198102938120931002938102938102310
46629381209310029381055598798755551234509876502938120931002938107
12329381209310029381053215000050000500500000502938120931002938107
78929381209310029381050987657750987500005005005002938120931002938107
12329381209310029381050000050055005000005000029381209310029381107
43229381209310029381050000050055555000005550002938120931002938107
98729381209310029381050000500050000050005000502938120931002938107
12329381209310029381055550000050000050500000502938120931002938107
38535858019238293817318231941010194071287109401270128319810293817
20531638938102938102310381029380192382938173182319712871094012707
12031983829381209310029381029381023103810293801923829381731823197
41010194551287112831981029381209310029381029381023103810293801927
```

Answer on page 109

SECRET COMMUNICATIONS

When communicating with other members of your team, it's a good idea to use a cipher to prevent enemy minions and criminal elements discovering your plans. Sometimes I use a very simple cipher to send messages to Team Extreme, and you can too.

I replace the first few letters of the alphabet with the letters XSTUPID. Dr X would never let his Skullmen suggest that as the code, and so he'll never crack it.

A	B	C	D	E	F	G	H	I	J	K	L
X	S	T	U	P	I	D	A	B	C	E	F

M	N	O	P	Q	R	S	T	U	V	W	X
G	H	J	K	L	M	N	O	Q	R	V	W

Y	Z
Y	Z

Can you read the message below using the cipher?

XTOBJH GXH BN OAP DMPXOPNO APMJ JI OAPG XFF

DATA FILE:
NINJA BIKE

In Jamaica they call a souped-up motorcycle a 'ninja', but I bet they never quite imagined this!

WINDSHIELD

For high-speed chases, I can crouch behind this to make the bike more aerodynamic.

FRONTAL FORK CASING

More than just a mud-guard. This protects the delicate brake components, and the wheel itself if I have to ram my way out of trouble.

TYRES

Solid tyres make punctures a thing of the past.

CHASSIS
The Action Man ninja bike is built on a light carbon frame to make stunts easier. But this isn't for showing off. Fighting on a moving vehicle is a stunt in itself, and I need all the help I can get.

ENGINE
The powerhouse of the bike. Underneath this cowling throbs a massive 750cc engine. There are much more powerful ones on the market, but this bike is so light that the engine doesn't have to work as hard to hit high speeds.

INTERNET SABOTAGE!

Action Man has retrieved a vital piece of data from Dr X in New York. He must now use the links of the internet to ship the data back to London, without running into any of Dr X's web sites. Help Action Man bring the data home and avoid letting it end up in Dr X's clutches. Which is the safest route?

THE CITY NEVER SLEEPS

The cops' car was parked over the road from his Street Racer. Action Man left his calling card under one of the windscreen wipers. That ought to help explain things; they weren't to know that they were caught in the middle of something big.

But then Action Man saw something inside the car. It was one of the cops' notebooks, belonging to some guy called Jimmy. The most recent entry made for interesting reading. It said: SOUTH SIDE ROBBERY, TIP-OFF FROM MAD GUY IN PURPLE!?

Action Man couldn't believe his eyes. Doctor X had actually tried to get him arrested. But that meant that right now X was somewhere in the city. Action Man spun on his heels and ran for the Street Racer.

The red sportscar tore down the street with a loud screech of burning rubber. Action Man kept his eyes peeled at every junction, kept looking down every side alley. The sun was setting and time was running short. It would be easier for X to escape at night.

Action Man pulled over and rested his head against the steering wheel. There was no denying it: X was gone. He had escaped again! Suddenly, Action Man realised how tired he was. It had been a very busy few days. The city never slept, but even Action Man needed to rest every now and then.

Wearily, he revved up the car and turned for home.

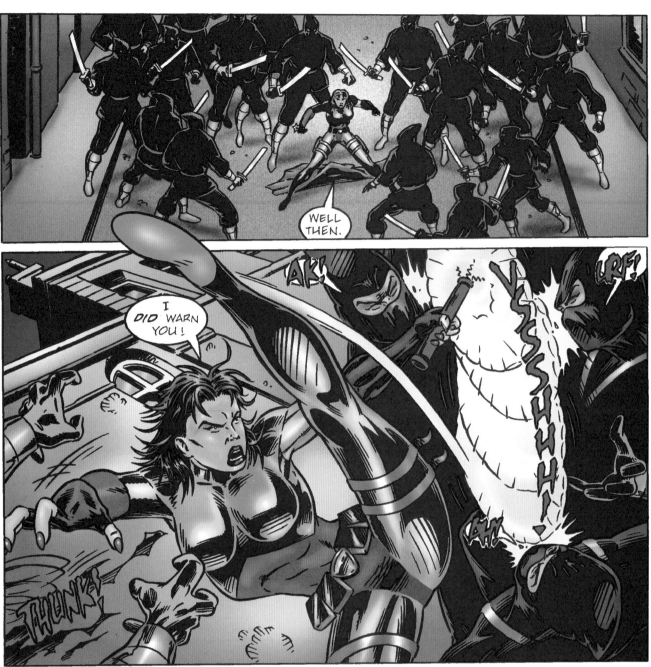

WIRE TANGLE

Which wire will defuse the bomb? In movies it's normally the red one, but X knows that, which is why he made all the wires the same colour! Action Man has one chance to stop X's bomb going off, but if he pulls the wrong wire, there's no telling what will happen! Help him get out of this tangle by finding the wire that leads to the detonator.

Which wire, A, B or C, must be cut ?

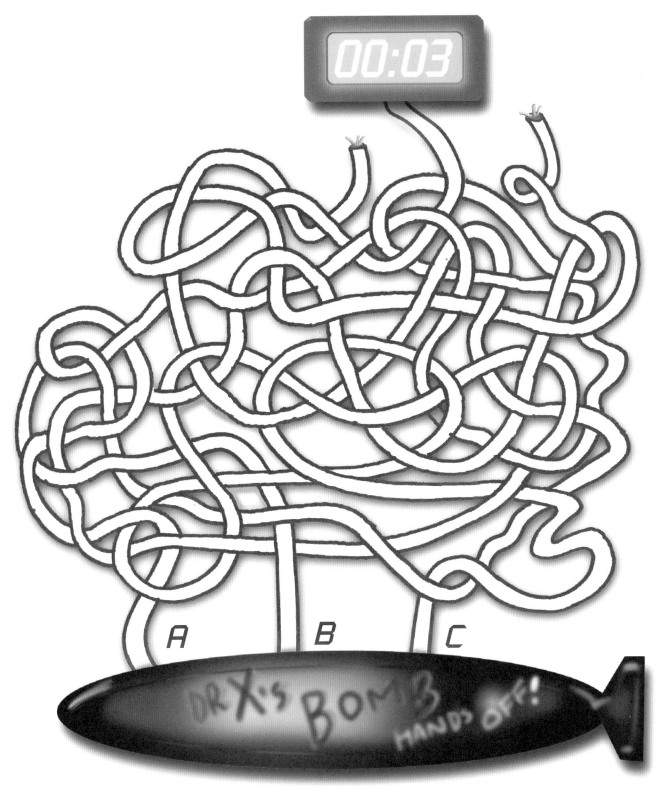

Answer on page 109.

ACTION MAN
INTELLIGENCE TEST

New York wasn't always called New York. Help Action Man find its original name by answering the questions and filling in the numbered boxes below. The letters that fill the red box down the left hand side will give you the answer you need.

1: An oriental assassin.
2: An animal with a trunk and tusks.
3: Opposite of loser.
4: Place where Action Man fought Doctor X in the first chapter.
5: An assignment.
6: Equipment for breathing underwater.
7: Something you use to dry yourself.
8: Tall building in New York. The _____ State Building.
9: Name of Action Man's dog.
10: Action Man's evil enemy.
11: Carries air for breathing underwater.
12: _____ Everest is the tallest in the world.

1 _ _ _ _ _ _
2 _ _ _ _ _ _ _ _
3 _ _ _ _ _ _
4 _ _ _ _ _ _ _
5 _ _ _ _ _ _
6 _ _ _ _ _
7 _ _ _ _ _
8 _ _ _ _ _ _
9 _ _ _ _
10 _ _ _ _ _ _ _
11 _ _ _ _ _ _ _
12 _ _ _ _ _

Answers on page 109.

THE URBAN JUNGLE

Even though it looks like home, the city can be the most dangerous environment of all. Criminals have the perfect camouflage: they look just like everybody else!

WILD ANIMALS

Cars won't charge you like a herd of elephants, or hunt you down like a cheetah, but they can be just as deadly. Use zebra and pelican crossings wherever possible, and look both ways before you cross the road.

DANGEROUS PLACES

No glaciers, sand dunes, swamps or whirlpools in the city, but that doesn't mean that the whole place is safe. Stay away from building sites, railway lines and anywhere else where you shouldn't be. If a sign says "KEEP OUT" then keep out! That's what I would do.

AFTER DARK

The city provides more light at night than you'd ever get in a jungle, but that doesn't mean it's safe. Try and stick to well-lit roads, or to be indoors before night falls.

CROOKS, MINIONS & SKULLMEN

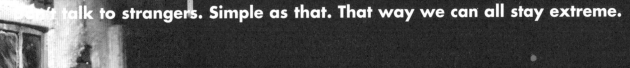
Don't talk to strangers. Simple as that. That way we can all stay extreme.

LIVING IN THE PAST... OR IS IT?

My Power Ninja suit is one of my most fearsome uniforms, but people are often surprised at how useful it is. You wouldn't think that there would be much call for old-fashioned martial arts in this modern world of tanks, guns and planes, but sometimes it's the best, fastest way to complete a mission.

CONFUSING THE ENEMY
If I have a particularly high-profile job, but want to keep anonymous, what better way than to sneak in wearing the ninja gear? I can wear it under normal clothes, so that when I find myself in the spotlight, everyone's so surprised to see a ninja they're less likely to see my face!

ORBITAL MISSIONS

The main problem with space missions is the use of weapons. You can't fire powerful projectile weapons on a space station; one puncture in the hull and you've lost all your air. So low-tech weapons are the best ones to use. And nothing prepares you for a zero gravity environment like all the acrobatics you have to do in training!

DRY RUNS

Some of my martial arts work might seem useless, but it has always paid off. I've never used judo to defeat a Skullman, but it has taught me how to land properly if I ever fall, and that's saved my life on several occasions. Kendo is no use in combat (bamboo sticks are hard to find in the middle of a mission), but I've used it to intimidate enemies in the past. And nothing can beat the all round training I get from martial arts. It keeps me fit and ready for action, and that's always important.

THE END...?

There wasn't much to Action Man's safe house. Just a bed, a kitchen and a bathroom. There was a lounge but most of the space in there was crammed with his global monitoring system, a huge computer. The spare bedroom was packed with discarded equipment. It wasn't much, but it was home for now.

There was desert sand in his hair. Tibetan mud was caught under his fingernails. His lips were blistered from the Himalayan cold. His cheeks were burned by the African sun. There were bruises on his legs from the fight in New York. Cyberspace had given him a headache. It had been a rough couple of days.

He was in the bath when the alarm went off. There was trouble somewhere in the world, and Doctor X was on the rampage again. Ships were disappearing off the coast of Australia. Action Man cancelled the alarm and lay back in the bubbles, thinking. He had a job to do, no matter what the risk.

Wrapped in a towel, he started to assemble a mission kit. He'd need to stealth his way over there. And he'd need some diving gear. Maybe a spare hang glider. That should do it. He could get airport clearance for take off in twenty minutes. Hey, maybe he could vote himself a holiday once the mission was over. Australia was supposed to be nice this time of year.

ANSWERS

Answers to page 19.

Answers to page 44.

M	O	U	N	T	A	I	N	S	K	E
A	R	I	C	A	N	N	H	H	A	V
I	Y	C	N	N	A	D	A	E	Z	E
A	E	R	P	O	N	T	I	B	E	T	R
S	T	C	E	N	X	A	A	P	L	E
H	I	M	A	L	A	Y	A	S	O	S
E	Y	S	K	L	A	W	G	D	J	T
R	S	W	S	A	P	A	N	E	I	R
P	E	R	L	L	A	M	A	S	N	A
A	J	G	H	J	I	T	R	E	D	E

Answer to page 48.

Continued over...

Answer to page 68.

Answer to page 92.

ANTI-VIRUS CODE: 7+8÷3=5

Answers to page 104.

1: NINJA
2: ELEPHANT
3 WINNER
4: AFRICA
5: MISSION
6: SCUBA
7: TOWEL
8: EMPIRE
9: RAID
10: DOCTOR X
11: AQUALUNG
12: MOUNT

The hidden word is New Amsterdam.

Answer to page 93.

XTBJH GXH BN OAP DMPXOPNO APMJ JI
OAPG XFF.

ACTION MAN IS THE GREATEST HERO OF
THEM ALL.

Answer to page 96.

C.

Answers to page 103.

C.

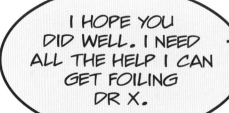

I HOPE YOU DID WELL. I NEED ALL THE HELP I CAN GET FOILING DR X.